CW00670334

THE
LEGENDARY
DAY
LIFE

"A life worth living is a life worth recording."

Jim Rohn

Congratulations on taking action to begin your journaling practice with the Legendary Life Journals. You now stand amongst legends. Many of history's preeminent leaders, geniuses and artists kept a daily journal. The Roman Emperor Marcus Aurelius, Albert Einstein, Thomas Edison, Frida Kahlo, Leonardo da Vinci, Beethoven, Benjamin Franklin, Isaac Newton, and Pablo Picasso are just a handful of visionaries who benefited from the practice of keeping a journal.

Journaling is a practical and accessible way to stay connected to your inner self, your body, your dreams and your purpose in life. The Legendary Day Life Journal will help you clarify your thinking, prioritise, be thankful and accomplish your most important tasks while simultaneously serving to inspire, motivate, and centre you.

Here's just a few of the benefits that you can expect to see from a regular journaling practice:

- Better Organisation
- Improved Judgment and Decision Making
- Refined Demeanour
- Enhanced Intention
- Positive Reinforcement

Ambitious, successful, happy and creative people are always working towards many goals. Journals are ideal tools to optimise the process of defining, tracking, manifesting and accelerating achievement of these goals. The Legendary Day Life Journal will empower you to maintain a record of the progress you've made towards your goals and their associated actions while keeping you motivated and inspired as you progress on your journey towards reaching them.

The art of recording your thoughts, wishes and musings with pen and paper have a great physical and mental impact. It allows you to collect otherwise lost insights and gratitude, gives you the ability to analyse the progress you have made and enables you to easily assess where you are, where you are going and where you have been.

New to journaling and not sure how to start? Here's some tips to help you get started:

- Be honest and authentic (write like no one else is going to read it).
- Forget about grammar and spelling when you write.
- Writing by hand in a physical journal such as the Legendary Life Journals (as opposed to journaling on a phone, tablet or laptop) promotes better memory recall.
- Adopt cursive writing to get your thoughts out faster.

Don't overthink your writing. Just start writing whatever is on your mind. The point is to write about your thoughts — not publish a polished article.

In order to maximise the value of your journaling time be sure to eliminate distractions: Turn off the TV, put your phone on airplane mode, close the door and strive for privacy. Our minds are most creative when we get the chance to be on our own. "Writing accesses the left hemisphere of the brain, which is analytical and rational," says Maud Purcell, a psychotherapist and journaling expert. "While your left brain is occupied, your right brain is free to do what it does best, i.e. create, intuit and feel. In this way, writing removes mental blocks and allows us to use more of our brainpower to better understand ourselves and the world around us."

Judy Willis MD, a neurologist, and former classroom teacher explains, "The practice of writing can enhance the brain's intake, processing, retaining, and retrieving of information… it promotes the brain's attentive focus … boosts long-term memory, illuminates patterns, gives the brain time for reflection, and when well-guided, is a source of conceptual development and stimulus of the brain's highest cognition."

Following are just some of the key benefits that can be expected from engaging in a regular journaling practice. The research-based format of the Legendary Life Journals was designed to:

- Develop a sense of gratitude.
- Provide a place and time to focus on the positive.
- Allow you to reflect and acknowledge progress on projects, initiatives and goals.
- Furnish a fresh perspective.
- Orient you from scarcity to abundance.
- Create a safe space to "discuss" things that

you feel you can't discuss with anyone else.

- Allow you to uncover the things weighing on your mind affecting your behaviour.
- Help you differentiate personal issues from professional ones.
- Provide you a private, healthy place to vent emotions.
- Enable you to separate symptoms from causes.
- Help you objectively examine feelings, emotions and events.
- Empower you to clarify and examine your motivations for actions and decisions.
- Analyse causes for the behavior of others in an unemotional, balanced manner.
- Reconnect you with what energises you and focuses your energy.
- Improve your self-awareness.
- Provide you with a concrete, visible list of the positive things in your life.

The Power of Habit:

There's one big thing to keep in mind. You will never achieve any of the amazing benefits of journaling unless you actually journal regularly. That means you must create a journaling practice that is also a habit. Once journaling becomes a habit it will be like second nature.

A journaling habit means that you will never "forget" to journal, "not have time" to journal, or be "too tired" to journal. On the contrary, it will be something that you instinctively feel that you have to do to have a fulfilling day. Don't believe us? Just consider these examples: You don't forget to brush your teeth, right? You always have time to drink your morning coffee or tea, don't you? And we'd bet that you're rarely "too tired" to check your social media feeds one last time prior to going to sleep at night. Why is that? It's because you have made either a conscious or unconscious choice at some point in your life to make those tasks habits as opposed to hobbies.

Habits are hugely powerful. People develop some habits that they perform for the rest of their lives with very little thought as to their continued value or detriment to their dreams and goals.

It may shock you to learn that on average, around 45% of our activities on a given day are habitual, performed automatically without us thinking about them. Generally, it takes between two and three months to form a new habit. Once a habit is entrenched, the practice becomes like brushing your teeth.

Habits have significant impact on every aspect of life. Therefore, it's very important to perform frequent self-assessments on your habits to determine which ones you need to modify or get rid of and which new habits you should develop that could better serve you and your goals. Habits must be audited and assessed on a regular basis, as once a habit is truly ingrained in a person's psyche it is performed outside the spectrum of conscious thought. This can be good or bad as habits can be working towards either creating or destroying your dreams and goals. We believe that in order to Live your Legend, you need to take control of the activities you perform daily.

"The difference between an amateur and a professional is in their habits. An amateur has amateur habits. A professional has professional habits." Steven Pressfield

Ok, so how do you actually go about the process of building your professional journaling habit? According to Charles Duhigg in his book, "The Power of Habit" there are four steps to creating a habit:

I. Cues

First, there is a cue. This is a trigger that tells your brain to go into automatic mode, and which habit to use. Cues can be almost anything, from a visual trigger to a time of day, an emotion, a sequence of thoughts, the company of particular people, etc.

In regards to journaling the cue might be seeing the journal itself in a specific place at a specific time every day. Maybe your journal is on your nightstand where you will see it right before you go to bed and right when you wake up in the morning.

II. Routines

Next, there is the routine. This can be physical, mental, or emotional. Routines can be incredibly complex or fantastically simple.

To make journaling a part of your routine you need to choose a specific part of your day to journal and sequence the activity in line with another existing habit. For example, maybe your morning routine is to wake up, make coffee, check your phone and then get ready for work. So in this example maybe you leave your journal next to your coffee maker and you sequence your journaling after your coffee. Now your new routine is to wake up, make coffee, journal, check your phone and then get ready for work.

III. Rewards

Finally, there is the reward. This helps your brain figure out if this particular loop is worth remembering for the future. Rewards can range from food or drugs that cause physical sensations, to emotional payoffs, such as the feelings of pride that accompany praise or self-congratulation.

To continue with our example from the "Routines" section: If caffeine is your thing, make that the reward. You do your journaling while the coffee is brewing but don't allow yourself to drink any java until you finish your journaling. That's your reward. If you are journaling in the evening and enjoy a glass of wine then maybe that's your reward. Or maybe it's a bite of chocolate. We all have our preferred treat. Use that as your reward. Once the habit becomes ingrained the reward won't be as important anymore. However, it will help you during the initial habit formation phase.

You should set small daily rewards such as the examples above for accomplishing your daily journaling practice. Additionally, you should also set a larger reward for sticking to your journaling habit consistently over the course of a fixed amount of time. We suggest the time period you use be 66 days. Why 66 days? That's not a random number. That's the average amount of days that scientists estimate is required to form a new habit. So figure out something a bit luxurious that you've been wanting for a while. Maybe it's a new, designer bag for work, maybe it's a new phone or gadget. Then set that as the master reward that you will buy yourself after completing 66 days in a row of your journaling practice.

IV. The Power of Belief

Our mind and spirit are not always aligned, even when we want them to be. Everything you do happily and successfully in life, you have to do while believing, truly believing, that it is the right thing to pursue. Therefore, while adopting a new habit like journaling, it is important to not only logically understand the value of the practice but to fully commit to believing in journaling and to the power that it can have to dramatically improve your life.

Here's a visualisation technique you can implement every time you finish journaling. This will help you establish and reinforce your belief around the power of journaling and align your mind and spirit around your practice.

- Simply hold your journal close to your heart and visualise the good that will come from your practice. See your Legendary Life unfold and take place in your mind's eye down to the smallest details. You may be surprised at how quickly and easily you achieve your goals when you commit to an unwavering belief that there is simply no other possibility to do otherwise.

You will most likely find that this visualisation technique will become unnecessary once you've established your practice as a habit. But until then it's a good idea to end your journaling with this simple belief exercise.

Final thoughts:

People tend to maintain their good habits pretty well when life is stable. However, in times of stress or in moments of difficulty, the positive habits that we worked so hard to achieve, such as exercising regularly, eating healthy or journaling, are far more vulnerable. When you experience these stressful periods, that's the time to acknowledge what you are dealing with, remind yourself it's only temporary and most importantly, recommit to staying consistent and prioritising your Legendary Life journaling practice (as well as your other positive habits) as those are the times your positive habits will help you the most.

So, how do you do that? Well, one way is to connect with accountability partners via a positive, like minded community, either online or IRL ("in real life") that will help you create and maintain your positive habits, your belief in yourself, your dreams, and your goal for Living Your Legend. Join positive Facebook groups where change seems possible, follow people and organisations that you are inspired by, and by all means connect with us and our community at Legendary Life across any and all of our platforms.

The potential for the change we are seeking to happen in ourselves seems more real when we see it in somebody else's eyes, read it in their words or hear it in their voice. Focus your time, physically and online, with people who share your beliefs that life can be outstanding and are, like you, summoning this positive energy. And conversely, avoid people who are constantly approaching life from a negative or cynical mindset. This is your time to thrive! This is your time to Live Your Legend!

● ● ●

Date: /   /

"We are all of us stars, and we deserve to twinkle".
- Marilyn Monroe

● *I'm thankful for* ....
....
....
....

● *Today I look forward to* ....
....
....
....

● *How can I make myself feel good today?* ....
....
....
....

● *What can I do today in order to bring me closer*
to my goals? ....
....
....

● *What is the most important thing for me to do*
today? ....
....
....

● *I am* ....
....
....
....

"Love the climb" - Gary Vaynerchuk

● *I'm thankful for* ....
....
....
....

● *Today I look forward to* ....
....
....
....

● *How can I make myself feel good today?*...........
....
....
....

● *What can I do today in order to bring me closer to my goals?*...
....
....

● *What is the most important thing for me to do today?*..
....
....

● *I am* ....
....
....
....

Date: /   /

"Knowledge is of no value unless you put it into practice." - Anton Chekhov

⬣ *I'm thankful for* ....
....
....
....

⬣ *Today I look forward to* ....
....
....
....

⬣ *How can I make myself feel good today?* ....
....
....
....

⬣ *What can I do today in order to bring me closer to my goals?* ....
....
....

⬣ *What is the most important thing for me to do today?* ....
....
....

⬣ *I am* ....
....
....
....

Date: /   /

"The best is the enemy of the good." - Voltaire

● *I'm thankful for* ....
....
....
....

● *Today I look forward to* ....
....
....
....

● *How can I make myself feel good today?* ....
....
....
....

● *What can I do today in order to bring me closer to my goals?* ....
....
....

● *What is the most important thing for me to do today?* ....
....
....

● *I am* ....
....
....
....

Date: /   /

"Fall in love with the process, and the results will come." - Eric Thomas

● *I'm thankful for* ....
....
....
....

● *Today I look forward to* ....
....
....
....

● *How can I make myself feel good today?* ....
....
....
....

● *What can I do today in order to bring me closer to my goals?* ....
....
....

● *What is the most important thing for me to do today?* ....
....
....

● *I am* ....
....
....
....

Date: / /

● *I'm thankful for* ....
....
....
....

● *Today I look forward to* ....
....
....
....

● *How can I make myself feel good today?* ....
....
....
....

● *What can I do today in order to bring me closer to my goals?* ....
....
....

● *What is the most important thing for me to do today?* ....
....
....

● *I am* ....
....
....
....

Date: /   /

"What You Do Today Can Improve All Your Tomorrows" - Ralph Marston

- **I'm thankful for** ....
....
....
....

- **Today I look forward to** ....
....
....
....

- **How can I make myself feel good today?** ....
....
....
....

- **What can I do today in order to bring me closer
to my goals?** ....
....
....

- **What is the most important thing for me to do
today?** ....
....
....

- **I am** ....
....
....
....

Do your thing!

Free Form / Brainstorm / Draw / Sketch
Doodle / Stream of Consciousness
Safe Space / Create / Vent / Manifest

Date: / /

"It does not matter how slowly you go as long as you do not stop." - Confucius

● *I'm thankful for* ....
....
....
....

● *Today I look forward to* ....
....
....
....

● *How can I make myself feel good today?* ....
....
....
....

● *What can I do today in order to bring me closer to my goals?* ....
....
....

● *What is the most important thing for me to do today?* ....
....
....

● *I am* ....
....
....
....

Date: /   /

"Seek first to understand and then to be understood." - Stephen Covey

● *I'm thankful for* ....
....
....
....

● *Today I look forward to* ....
....
....
....

● *How can I make myself feel good today?* ....
....
....
....

● *What can I do today in order to bring me closer to my goals?* ....
....
....

● *What is the most important thing for me to do today?* ....
....
....

● *I am* ....
....
....
....

*"You can do anything as long as you have the
passion, the drive, the focus, and the support."
- Sabrina Bryan*

● I'm thankful for ....
....
....
....

● Today I look forward to ....
....
....
....

● How can I make myself feel good today? ....
....
....
....

● What can I do today in order to bring me closer
to my goals? ....
....
....

● What is the most important thing for me to do
today? ....
....
....

● I am ....
....
....
....

"The triumph can't be had without the struggle"
- Wilma Rudolph

● *I'm thankful for* ....
....
....
....

● *Today I look forward to* ....
....
....
....

● *How can I make myself feel good today?* ....
....
....
....

● *What can I do today in order to bring me closer*
to my goals? ....
....
....

● *What is the most important thing for me to do*
today? ....
....
....

● *I am* ....
....
....
....

"Courage is knowing what not to fear". - Plato

● *I'm thankful for* ....
....
....
....

● *Today I look forward to* ....
....
....
....

● *How can I make myself feel good today?* ....
....
....
....

● *What can I do today in order to bring me closer to my goals?* ....
....
....

● *What is the most important thing for me to do today?* ....
....
....

● *I am* ....
....
....
....

"Only when we are no longer afraid do we begin to live". - Dorothy Thompson

● *I'm thankful for* ....
....
....
....

● *Today I look forward to* ....
....
....
....

● *How can I make myself feel good today?* ....
....
....
....

● *What can I do today in order to bring me closer to my goals?* ....
....
....

● *What is the most important thing for me to do today?* ....
....
....

● *I am* ....
....
....
....

"Change brings opportunity." - Nido Qubein

⬢ *I'm thankful for* ....
....
....
....

⬢ *Today I look forward to* ....
....
....
....

⬢ *How can I make myself feel good today?* ....
....
....
....

⬢ *What can I do today in order to bring me closer*
to my goals? ....
....
....

⬢ *What is the most important thing for me to do*
today? ....
....
....

⬢ *I am* ....
....
....
....

Do your thing!

Free Form / Brainstorm / Draw / Sketch
Doodle / Stream of Consciousness
Safe Space / Create / Vent / Manifest

Date: / /

● *I'm thankful for* ....
....
....
....

● *Today I look forward to* ....
....
....
....

● *How can I make myself feel good today?* ....
....
....
....

● *What can I do today in order to bring me closer to my goals?* ....
....
....

● *What is the most important thing for me to do today?* ....
....
....

● *I am* ....
....
....
....

"If you don't love what you do, you won't do it with much conviction or passion." - Mia Hamm

● *I'm thankful for* ....
....
....
....

● *Today I look forward to* ....
....
....
....

● *How can I make myself feel good today?* ....
....
....
....

● *What can I do today in order to bring me closer to my goals?* ....
....
....

● *What is the most important thing for me to do today?* ....
....
....

● *I am* ....
....
....
....

"I believe in the person that I want to become."
- Lana Del Ray

● *I'm thankful for* ....
....
....
....

● *Today I look forward to* ....
....
....
....

● *How can I make myself feel good today?* ....
....
....
....

● *What can I do today in order to bring me closer to my goals?* ....
....
....

● *What is the most important thing for me to do today?* ....
....
....

● *I am* ....
....
....
....

Date: / /

"Early to bed and early to rise makes a man healthy, wealthy and wise." - Benjamin Franklin

● *I'm thankful for* ....
....
....
....

● *Today I look forward to* ....
....
....
....

● *How can I make myself feel good today?* ....
....
....
....

● *What can I do today in order to bring me closer to my goals?* ....
....
....

● *What is the most important thing for me to do today?* ....
....
....

● *I am* ....
....
....
....

"Work harder on yourself than you do on your job"
- Jim Rohn

● *I'm thankful for* ....
....
....
....

● *Today I look forward to* ....
....
....
....

● *How can I make myself feel good today?* ....
....
....
....

● *What can I do today in order to bring me closer to my goals?* ....
....
....

● *What is the most important thing for me to do today?* ....
....
....

● *I am* ....
....
....
....

"We must all either wear out or rust out, every one of us. My choice is to wear out."
- Theodore Roosevelt

● *I'm thankful for* ....
....
....
....

● *Today I look forward to* ....
....
....
....

● *How can I make myself feel good today?* ....
....
....
....

● *What can I do today in order to bring me closer to my goals?* ....
....
....

● *What is the most important thing for me to do today?* ....
....
....

● *I am* ....
....
....
....

"You are only entitled to the action, never to its fruits." - Bhagavad Gita

● *I'm thankful for* ....
....
....
....

● *Today I look forward to* ....
....
....
....

● *How can I make myself feel good today?* ....
....
....
....

● *What can I do today in order to bring me closer to my goals?* ....
....
....

● *What is the most important thing for me to do today?* ....
....
....

● *I am* ....
....
....
....

Do your thing!

Free Form / Brainstorm / Draw / Sketch
Doodle / Stream of Consciousness
Safe Space / Create / Vent / Manifest

Date: / /

"Space I can recover. Time, never."
- Napoleon Bonaparte

● *I'm thankful for* ....
....
....
....

● *Today I look forward to* ....
....
....
....

● *How can I make myself feel good today?* ....
....
....
....

● *What can I do today in order to bring me closer*
to my goals? ....
....
....

● *What is the most important thing for me to do*
today? ....
....
....

● *I am* ....
....
....
....

"To improve is to change, so to be perfect is to have changed often." - Winston Churchill

● *I'm thankful for* ....
....
....
....

● *Today I look forward to* ....
....
....
....

● *How can I make myself feel good today?* ....
....
....
....

● *What can I do today in order to bring me closer to my goals?* ....
....
....

● *What is the most important thing for me to do today?* ....
....
....

● *I am* ....
....
....
....

Date: / /

"No one saves us but ourselves. No one can and no one may." - Buddha

● *I'm thankful for* ....
....
....
....

● *Today I look forward to* ....
....
....
....

● *How can I make myself feel good today?* ....
....
....
....

● *What can I do today in order to bring me closer to my goals?* ....
....
....

● *What is the most important thing for me to do today?* ....
....
....

● *I am* ....
....
....
....

"The only way life gets better for you is when you get better. Better is not something you wish for; better is something you become." - Jim Rohn

● *I'm thankful for* ....
....
....
....

● *Today I look forward to* ....
....
....
....

● *How can I make myself feel good today?* ....
....
....
....

● *What can I do today in order to bring me closer to my goals?* ....
....
....

● *What is the most important thing for me to do today?* ....
....
....

● *I am* ....
....
....
....

Date: / /

"I do not know anyone who has got to the top without hard work. That is the recipe. It will not always get you to the top, but should get you pretty near." - Margaret Thatcher

● *I'm thankful for* ....
....
....
....

● *Today I look forward to* ....
....
....
....

● *How can I make myself feel good today?* ....
....
....
....

● *What can I do today in order to bring me closer to my goals?* ....
....
....

● *What is the most important thing for me to do today?* ....
....
....

● *I am* ....
....
....
....

Date: / /

> *"It always seems impossible until it's done."*
> *- Nelson Mandela*

- **I'm thankful for** ....
  ....
  ....
  ....

- **Today I look forward to** ....
  ....
  ....
  ....

- **How can I make myself feel good today?** ....
  ....
  ....
  ....

- **What can I do today in order to bring me closer to my goals?** ....
  ....
  ....

- **What is the most important thing for me to do today?** ....
  ....
  ....

- **I am** ....
  ....
  ....
  ....

"If you feel like there's something out there that you're supposed to be doing, if you have a passion for it, then stop wishing and just do it."
- Wanda Sykes

● *I'm thankful for* ....
....
....
....

● *Today I look forward to* ....
....
....
....

● *How can I make myself feel good today?* ....
....
....
....

● *What can I do today in order to bring me closer to my goals?* ....
....
....

● *What is the most important thing for me to do today?* ....
....
....

● *I am* ....
....
....
....

Do your thing!

Free Form / Brainstorm / Draw / Sketch
Doodle / Stream of Consciousness
Safe Space / Create / Vent / Manifest

Date: / /

● *I'm thankful for* ....
....
....
....

● *Today I look forward to* ....
....
....
....

● *How can I make myself feel good today?* ....
....
....
....

● *What can I do today in order to bring me closer to my goals?* ....
....
....

● *What is the most important thing for me to do today?* ....
....
....

● *I am* ....
....
....
....

Date: / /

"Only she who attempts the absurd can achieve the impossible." - Robin Morgan

● *I'm thankful for* ....
....
....
....

● *Today I look forward to* ....
....
....
....

● *How can I make myself feel good today?* ....
....
....
....

● *What can I do today in order to bring me closer to my goals?* ....
....
....

● *What is the most important thing for me to do today?* ....
....
....

● *I am* ....
....
....
....

"You have to expect things of yourself before you can do them." - Michael Jordan

⬤ *I'm thankful for* ....
....
....
....

⬤ *Today I look forward to* ....
....
....
....

⬤ *How can I make myself feel good today?* ....
....
....
....

⬤ *What can I do today in order to bring me closer to my goals?* ....
....
....

⬤ *What is the most important thing for me to do today?* ....
....
....

⬤ *I am* ....
....
....
....

> *"Being defeated is often a temporary condition.*
> *Giving up is what makes it permanent."*
> *- Marilyn vos Savant*

● *I'm thankful for* ....

....

....

....

● *Today I look forward to* ....

....

....

....

● *How can I make myself feel good today?* ....

....

....

....

● *What can I do today in order to bring me closer*
to my goals? ....

....

....

● *What is the most important thing for me to do*
today? ....

....

....

● *I am* ....

....

....

....

Date: / /

● **I'm thankful for** ....
....
....
....

● **Today I look forward to** ....
....
....
....

● **How can I make myself feel good today?** ....
....
....
....

● **What can I do today in order to bring me closer to my goals?** ....
....
....

● **What is the most important thing for me to do today?** ....
....
....

● **I am** ....
....
....
....

Date: /   /

"If you aren't in over your head, how do you know how tall you are?" - T.S. Eliot

- **I'm thankful for** ....
....
....
....

- **Today I look forward to** ....
....
....
....

- **How can I make myself feel good today?** ....
....
....
....

- **What can I do today in order to bring me closer to my goals?** ....
....
....

- **What is the most important thing for me to do today?** ....
....
....

- **I am** ....
....
....
....

"Don't compromise yourself. You are all you've got. There is no yesterday, no tomorrow, it's all the same day." - Janis Joplin

⬢ *I'm thankful for* ....
....
....
....

⬢ *Today I look forward to* ....
....
....
....

⬢ *How can I make myself feel good today?* ....
....
....
....

⬢ *What can I do today in order to bring me closer to my goals?* ....
....
....

⬢ *What is the most important thing for me to do today?* ....
....
....

⬢ *I am* ....
....
....
....

Do your thing!

Free Form / Brainstorm / Draw / Sketch
Doodle / Stream of Consciousness
Safe Space / Create / Vent / Manifest

Date: / /

"Passion is energy. Feel the power that comes from focusing on what excites you." - Oprah Winfrey

● *I'm thankful for* ....
....
....
....

● *Today I look forward to* ....
....
....
....

● *How can I make myself feel good today?* ....
....
....
....

● *What can I do today in order to bring me closer to my goals?* ....
....
....

● *What is the most important thing for me to do today?* ....
....
....

● *I am* ....
....
....
....

"There are no traffic jams along the extra mile."
- Roger Staubach

● *I'm thankful for* ....
....
....
....

● *Today I look forward to* ....
....
....
....

● *How can I make myself feel good today?* ....
....
....
....

● *What can I do today in order to bring me closer to my goals?* ....
....
....

● *What is the most important thing for me to do today?* ....
....
....

● *I am* ....
....
....
....

"I've found that luck is quite predictable. If you want more luck, take more chances. Be more active. Show up more often." - Brian Tracy

● *I'm thankful for* ....
....
....
....

● *Today I look forward to* ....
....
....
....

● *How can I make myself feel good today?* ....
....
....
....

● *What can I do today in order to bring me closer to my goals?* ....
....
....

● *What is the most important thing for me to do today?* ....
....
....

● *I am* ....
....
....
....

Date: / /

● *I'm thankful for* ....
....
....
....

● *Today I look forward to* ....
....
....
....

● *How can I make myself feel good today?* ....
....
....
....

● *What can I do today in order to bring me closer to my goals?* ....
....
....

● *What is the most important thing for me to do today?* ....
....
....

● *I am* ....
....
....
....

"Every strike brings me closer to the next home run." - Babe Ruth

● *I'm thankful for* ....
....
....
....

● *Today I look forward to* ....
....
....
....

● *How can I make myself feel good today?* ....
....
....
....

● *What can I do today in order to bring me closer to my goals?* ....
....
....

● *What is the most important thing for me to do today?* ....
....
....

● *I am* ....
....
....
....

Date: / /

⬤ *I'm thankful for* ....
....
....
....

⬤ *Today I look forward to* ....
....
....
....

⬤ *How can I make myself feel good today?* ....
....
....
....

⬤ *What can I do today in order to bring me closer to my goals?* ....
....
....

⬤ *What is the most important thing for me to do today?* ....
....
....

⬤ *I am* ....
....
....
....

"The man who removes a mountain begins by carrying away small stones." - Chinese Proverb

● *I'm thankful for* ....
....
....
....

● *Today I look forward to* ....
....
....
....

● *How can I make myself feel good today?* ....
....
....
....

● *What can I do today in order to bring me closer to my goals?* ....
....
....

● *What is the most important thing for me to do today?* ....
....
....

● *I am* ....
....
....
....

Do your thing!

Free Form / Brainstorm / Draw / Sketch
Doodle / Stream of Consciousness
Safe Space / Create / Vent / Manifest

Date: /   /

"Small deeds done are better than great deeds planned." - Peter Marshall

- *I'm thankful for* ....
....
....
....

- *Today I look forward to* ....
....
....
....

- *How can I make myself feel good today?* ....
....
....
....

- *What can I do today in order to bring me closer to my goals?* ....
....
....

- *What is the most important thing for me to do today?* ....
....
....

- *I am* ....
....
....
....

"Look at a day when you are supremely satisfied at the end. It's not a day when you lounge around doing nothing; it's when you've had everything to do, and you've done it." - Margaret Thatcher

● **I'm thankful for** ....
....
....
....

● **Today I look forward to** ....
....
....
....

● **How can I make myself feel good today?** ....
....
....
....

● **What can I do today in order to bring me closer to my goals?** ....
....
....

● **What is the most important thing for me to do today?** ....
....
....

● **I am** ....
....
....
....

Date: / /

"Our greatest glory is not in never falling, but in rising every time we fall." - Confucius

- *I'm thankful for* ....
  ....
  ....
  ....

- *Today I look forward to* ....
  ....
  ....
  ....

- *How can I make myself feel good today?* ....
  ....
  ....
  ....

- *What can I do today in order to bring me closer to my goals?* ....
  ....
  ....

- *What is the most important thing for me to do today?* ....
  ....
  ....

- *I am* ....
  ....
  ....
  ....

Date: / /

"Never give up on something that you can't go a day without thinking about." - Winston Churchill

⬣ *I'm thankful for* ....
....
....
....

⬣ *Today I look forward to* ....
....
....
....

⬣ *How can I make myself feel good today?* ....
....
....
....

⬣ *What can I do today in order to bring me closer to my goals?* ....
....
....

⬣ *What is the most important thing for me to do today?* ....
....
....

⬣ *I am* ....
....
....
....

Date: /   /

*"Failure in and of itself is not a bad thing. But failing
to learn from it is inexcusable." - Alison Levine*

- *I'm thankful for* ....
  ....
  ....
  ....

- *Today I look forward to* ....
  ....
  ....
  ....

- *How can I make myself feel good today?* ....
  ....
  ....
  ....

- *What can I do today in order to bring me closer
  to my goals?* ....
  ....
  ....

- *What is the most important thing for me to do
  today?* ....
  ....
  ....

- *I am* ....
  ....
  ....
  ....

Date: / /

"I hear and I forget. I see and I remember. I do and I understand." - Confucius

● *I'm thankful for* ....
....
....
....

● *Today I look forward to* ....
....
....
....

● *How can I make myself feel good today?* ....
....
....
....

● *What can I do today in order to bring me closer to my goals?* ....
....
....

● *What is the most important thing for me to do today?* ....
....
....

● *I am* ....
....
....
....

Date: /   /

"You don't have to be great to start, but you have to start to be great." - Zig Ziglar

- *I'm thankful for* ....
....
....
....

- *Today I look forward to* ....
....
....
....

- *How can I make myself feel good today?* ....
....
....
....

- *What can I do today in order to bring me closer to my goals?* ....
....
....

- *What is the most important thing for me to do today?* ....
....
....

- *I am* ....
....
....
....

Do your thing!

Free Form / Brainstorm / Draw / Sketch
Doodle / Stream of Consciousness
Safe Space / Create / Vent / Manifest

Date: / /

● *I'm thankful for* ....
....
....
....

● *Today I look forward to* ....
....
....
....

● *How can I make myself feel good today?* ....
....
....
....

● *What can I do today in order to bring me closer
to my goals?* ....
....
....

● *What is the most important thing for me to do
today?* ....
....
....

● *I am* ....
....
....
....

Date: / /

"Learn the rules like a pro, so you can break them like an artist." - Pablo Picasso

● *I'm thankful for* ....
....
....
....

● *Today I look forward to* ....
....
....
....

● *How can I make myself feel good today?* ....
....
....
....

● *What can I do today in order to bring me closer to my goals?* ....
....
....

● *What is the most important thing for me to do today?* ....
....
....

● *I am* ....
....
....
....

"The beautiful thing about learning is that no one can take it away from you." - B.B. King

● *I'm thankful for* ....
....
....
....

● *Today I look forward to* ....
....
....
....

● *How can I make myself feel good today?* ....
....
....
....

● *What can I do today in order to bring me closer to my goals?* ....
....
....

● *What is the most important thing for me to do today?* ....
....
....

● *I am* ....
....
....
....

Date: / /

> *"It doesn't matter how many times you fail. You only have to be right once and then everyone can tell you that you are an overnight success."*
> *- Mark Cuban*

● *I'm thankful for* ....
....
....
....

● *Today I look forward to* ....
....
....
....

● *How can I make myself feel good today?* ....
....
....
....

● *What can I do today in order to bring me closer to my goals?* ....
....
....

● *What is the most important thing for me to do today?* ....
....
....

● *I am* ....
....
....
....

"No matter how tough the chase is, you should always have the dream you saw on the first day. It'll keep you motivated and rescue you (from any weak thoughts)." - Jack Ma

● *I'm thankful for* ....
....
....
....

● *Today I look forward to* ....
....
....
....

● *How can I make myself feel good today?* ....
....
....
....

● *What can I do today in order to bring me closer to my goals?* ....
....
....

● *What is the most important thing for me to do today?* ....
....
....

● *I am* ....
....
....
....

Date: / /

"No matter how many goals you have achieved you must set your sights on a higher one."
- Jessica Savitch

● *I'm thankful for* ....
....
....
....

● *Today I look forward to* ....
....
....
....

● *How can I make myself feel good today?* ....
....
....
....

● *What can I do today in order to bring me closer to my goals?* ....
....
....

● *What is the most important thing for me to do today?* ....
....
....

● *I am* ....
....
....
....

"A great leader's courage to fulfill his vision comes from passion, not position." - John C. Maxwell

● *I'm thankful for* ....
....
....
....

● *Today I look forward to* ....
....
....
....

● *How can I make myself feel good today?* ....
....
....
....

● *What can I do today in order to bring me closer to my goals?* ....
....
....

● *What is the most important thing for me to do today?* ....
....
....

● *I am* ....
....
....
....

Do your thing!

Free Form / Brainstorm / Draw / Sketch
Doodle / Stream of Consciousness
Safe Space / Create / Vent / Manifest

Date: /   /

● *I'm thankful for* ....
....
....
....

● *Today I look forward to* ....
....
....
....

● *How can I make myself feel good today?* ....
....
....
....

● *What can I do today in order to bring me closer
to my goals?* ....
....
....

● *What is the most important thing for me to do
today?* ....
....
....

● *I am* ....
....
....
....

"If people knew how hard I worked to achieve mastery, it wouldn't seem so wonderful after all."
- Michelangelo

● *I'm thankful for* ....
....
....
....

● *Today I look forward to* ....
....
....
....

● *How can I make myself feel good today?* ....
....
....
....

● *What can I do today in order to bring me closer to my goals?* ....
....
....

● *What is the most important thing for me to do today?* ....
....
....

● *I am* ....
....
....
....

Date: / /

"Everything you've ever wanted is on the other side of fear." - George Addair

● *I'm thankful for* ....
....
....
....

● *Today I look forward to* ....
....
....
....

● *How can I make myself feel good today?* ....
....
....
....

● *What can I do today in order to bring me closer to my goals?* ....
....
....

● *What is the most important thing for me to do today?* ....
....
....

● *I am* ....
....
....
....

"Success is nothing more than a few simple disciplines, practiced every day." - Jim Rohn

● *I'm thankful for* ....
....
....
....

● *Today I look forward to* ....
....
....
....

● *How can I make myself feel good today?* ....
....
....
....

● *What can I do today in order to bring me closer to my goals?* ....
....
....

● *What is the most important thing for me to do today?* ....
....
....

● *I am* ....
....
....
....

"Every calling is great when greatly pursued."
- Oliver Wendell Holmes

● *I'm thankful for* ....
....
....
....

● *Today I look forward to* ....
....
....
....

● *How can I make myself feel good today?* ....
....
....
....

● *What can I do today in order to bring me closer*
to my goals? ....
....
....

● *What is the most important thing for me to do*
today? ....
....
....

● *I am* ....
....
....
....

Date: / /

"A successful person is one who can lay a firm foundation with the bricks that others throw at him or her." - David Brinkley

● *I'm thankful for* ....
....
....
....

● *Today I look forward to* ....
....
....
....

● *How can I make myself feel good today?* ....
....
....
....

● *What can I do today in order to bring me closer to my goals?* ....
....
....

● *What is the most important thing for me to do today?* ....
....
....

● *I am* ....
....
....
....

"Failure is acceptable. But not trying is a whole different ball park." - Michael Jordan

● **I'm thankful for** ....

....

....

....

● **Today I look forward to** ....

....

....

....

● **How can I make myself feel good today?** ....

....

....

....

● **What can I do today in order to bring me closer to my goals?** ....

....

....

● **What is the most important thing for me to do today?** ....

....

....

● **I am** ....

....

....

....

Do your thing!

Free Form / Brainstorm / Draw / Sketch
Doodle / Stream of Consciousness
Safe Space / Create / Vent / Manifest

Date: / /

● *I'm thankful for* ....
....
....
....

● *Today I look forward to* ....
....
....
....

● *How can I make myself feel good today?* ....
....
....
....

● *What can I do today in order to bring me closer to my goals?* ....
....
....

● *What is the most important thing for me to do today?* ....
....
....

● *I am* ....
....
....
....

Date: / /

"What we do is never as important as how we do it." - Jane Nelson

● *I'm thankful for* ....
....
....
....

● *Today I look forward to* ....
....
....
....

● *How can I make myself feel good today?* ....
....
....
....

● *What can I do today in order to bring me closer to my goals?* ....
....
....

● *What is the most important thing for me to do today?* ....
....
....

● *I am* ....
....
....
....

Date: / /

"Don't assume a door is closed; push on it. Do not assume if it was closed yesterday that it was closed today." - Marian Wright Edelman

● *I'm thankful for* ....
....
....
....

● *Today I look forward to* ....
....
....
....

● *How can I make myself feel good today?* ....
....
....
....

● *What can I do today in order to bring me closer to my goals?* ....
....
....

● *What is the most important thing for me to do today?* ....
....
....

● *I am* ....
....
....
....

"The beginning is always today." - Mary Shelley

● *I'm thankful for* ....
....
....
....

● *Today I look forward to* ....
....
....
....

● *How can I make myself feel good today?* ....
....
....
....

● *What can I do today in order to bring me closer to my goals?* ....
....
....

● *What is the most important thing for me to do today?* ....
....
....

● *I am* ....
....
....
....

Date: / /

*"The greatest mistake you can make in life is to be
continually fearing that you will make one."*
- Elbert Hubbard

● *I'm thankful for* ....
....
....
....

● *Today I look forward to* ....
....
....
....

● *How can I make myself feel good today?* ....
....
....
....

● *What can I do today in order to bring me closer
to my goals?* ....
....
....

● *What is the most important thing for me to do
today?* ....
....
....

● *I am* ....
....
....
....

"Work smart. Get things done. No nonsense. Move fast." - Susan Wojcicki

● *I'm thankful for* ....
....
....
....

● *Today I look forward to* ....
....
....
....

● *How can I make myself feel good today?* ....
....
....
....

● *What can I do today in order to bring me closer to my goals?* ....
....
....

● *What is the most important thing for me to do today?* ....
....
....

● *I am* ....
....
....
....

Date: /   /

*"You can, you should, and if you are brave enough
to start, you will." - Stephen King*

● *I'm thankful for* ....
....
....
....

● *Today I look forward to* ....
....
....
....

● *How can I make myself feel good today?* ....
....
....
....

● *What can I do today in order to bring me closer
to my goals?* ....
....
....

● *What is the most important thing for me to do
today?* ....
....
....

● *I am* ....
....
....
....

Do your thing!

Free Form / Brainstorm / Draw / Sketch
Doodle / Stream of Consciousness
Safe Space / Create / Vent / Manifest

Date: / /

"The struggle alone pleases us, not the victory."
- Blaise Pascal

● *I'm thankful for* ....
....
....
....

● *Today I look forward to* ....
....
....
....

● *How can I make myself feel good today?* ....
....
....
....

● *What can I do today in order to bring me closer to my goals?* ....
....
....

● *What is the most important thing for me to do today?* ....
....
....

● *I am* ....
....
....
....

Date: / /

"Opportunity dances with those who are already on the dance floor." - Jackson Browne

● *I'm thankful for* ....
....
....
....

● *Today I look forward to* ....
....
....
....

● *How can I make myself feel good today?* ....
....
....
....

● *What can I do today in order to bring me closer to my goals?* ....
....
....

● *What is the most important thing for me to do today?* ....
....
....

● *I am* ....
....
....
....

"The reward of a thing well done, is to have done it." - Ralph Waldo Emerson

● *I'm thankful for* ....
....
....
....

● *Today I look forward to* ....
....
....
....

● *How can I make myself feel good today?* ....
....
....
....

● *What can I do today in order to bring me closer to my goals?* ....
....
....

● *What is the most important thing for me to do today?* ....
....
....

● *I am* ....
....
....
....

"The best way to make your dreams come true is to wake up." - Muhammad Ali

- **I'm thankful for** ....
....
....
....

- **Today I look forward to** ....
....
....
....

- **How can I make myself feel good today?** ....
....
....
....

- **What can I do today in order to bring me closer to my goals?** ....
....
....

- **What is the most important thing for me to do today?** ....
....
....

- **I am** ....
....
....
....

"Don't give up at halftime. Concentrate on winning the second half." - Bear Bryant

● *I'm thankful for* ....
....
....
....

● *Today I look forward to* ....
....
....
....

● *How can I make myself feel good today?* ....
....
....
....

● *What can I do today in order to bring me closer to my goals?* ....
....
....

● *What is the most important thing for me to do today?* ....
....
....

● *I am* ....
....
....
....

"Freedom lies in being bold." - Robert Frost

● *I'm thankful for* ....
....
....
....

● *Today I look forward to* ....
....
....
....

● *How can I make myself feel good today?* ....
....
....
....

● *What can I do today in order to bring me closer to my goals?* ....
....
....

● *What is the most important thing for me to do today?* ....
....
....

● *I am* ....
....
....
....

"Little by little does the trick." - Aesop

● *I'm thankful for* ....
....
....
....

● *Today I look forward to* ....
....
....
....

● *How can I make myself feel good today?* ....
....
....
....

● *What can I do today in order to bring me closer to my goals?* ....
....
....

● *What is the most important thing for me to do today?* ....
....
....

● *I am* ....
....
....
....

Do your thing!

Free Form / Brainstorm / Draw / Sketch
Doodle / Stream of Consciousness
Safe Space / Create / Vent / Manifest

Date: / /

● *I'm thankful for* ....
....
....
....

● *Today I look forward to* ....
....
....
....

● *How can I make myself feel good today?* ....
....
....
....

● *What can I do today in order to bring me closer to my goals?* ....
....
....

● *What is the most important thing for me to do today?* ....
....
....

● *I am* ....
....
....
....

"Nobody who ever gave their best regretted it."
- George Halas

● *I'm thankful for* ....
....
....
....

● *Today I look forward to* ....
....
....
....

● *How can I make myself feel good today?* ....
....
....
....

● *What can I do today in order to bring me closer*
to my goals? ....
....
....

● *What is the most important thing for me to do*
today? ....
....
....

● *I am* ....
....
....
....

Date: / /

"Have the passion, take the action and magic will happen." - Bar Refaeli

● *I'm thankful for* ....
....
....
....

● *Today I look forward to* ....
....
....
....

● *How can I make myself feel good today?*..........
....
....
....

● *What can I do today in order to bring me closer to my goals?*..
....
....

● *What is the most important thing for me to do today?*..
....
....

● *I am* ....
....
....
....

Date: / /

"If everything was given to you, it wouldn't feel as good when you achieve it." - Annika Sörenstam

- *I'm thankful for* ....
  ....
  ....
  ....

- *Today I look forward to* ....
  ....
  ....
  ....

- *How can I make myself feel good today?* ....
  ....
  ....
  ....

- *What can I do today in order to bring me closer to my goals?* ....
  ....
  ....

- *What is the most important thing for me to do today?* ....
  ....
  ....

- *I am* ....
  ....
  ....
  ....

"Excellence is about outworking someone else."
- Marcus Lemonis

● *I'm thankful for* ....
....
....
....

● *Today I look forward to* ....
....
....
....

● *How can I make myself feel good today?* ....
....
....
....

● *What can I do today in order to bring me closer to my goals?* ....
....
....

● *What is the most important thing for me to do today?* ....
....
....

● *I am* ....
....
....
....

"Talent is cheaper than table salt. What separates the talented individual from the successful one is a lot of hard work." - Stephen King

● *I'm thankful for* ....
....
....
....

● *Today I look forward to* ....
....
....
....

● *How can I make myself feel good today?* ....
....
....
....

● *What can I do today in order to bring me closer to my goals?* ....
....
....

● *What is the most important thing for me to do today?* ....
....
....

● *I am* ....
....
....
....

Date: / /

- *I'm thankful for* ....
....
....
....

- *Today I look forward to* ....
....
....
....

- *How can I make myself feel good today?* ....
....
....
....

- *What can I do today in order to bring me closer to my goals?* ....
....
....

- *What is the most important thing for me to do today?* ....
....
....

- *I am* ....
....
....
....

Do your thing!

Free Form / Brainstorm / Draw / Sketch
Doodle / Stream of Consciousness
Safe Space / Create / Vent / Manifest

"To attain knowledge, add things everyday. To attain wisdom, remove things every day." - Lao Tse

- **I'm thankful for** ....
....
....
....

- **Today I look forward to** ....
....
....
....

- **How can I make myself feel good today?** ....
....
....
....

- **What can I do today in order to bring me closer to my goals?** ....
....
....

- **What is the most important thing for me to do today?** ....
....
....

- **I am** ....
....
....
....

Date: / /

● *I'm thankful for* ....
....
....
....

● *Today I look forward to* ....
....
....
....

● *How can I make myself feel good today?* ....
....
....
....

● *What can I do today in order to bring me closer to my goals?* ....
....
....

● *What is the most important thing for me to do today?* ....
....
....

● *I am* ....
....
....
....

"Pursue knowledge as though it is your life-blood, then you will know greatness!" - Monique Rockliffe

● *I'm thankful for* ....
....
....
....

● *Today I look forward to* ....
....
....
....

● *How can I make myself feel good today?* ....
....
....
....

● *What can I do today in order to bring me closer to my goals?* ....
....
....

● *What is the most important thing for me to do today?* ....
....
....

● *I am* ....
....
....
....

"Attitude is a choice. Happiness is a choice. Optimism is a choice. Kindness is a choice. Giving is a choice. Respect is a choice. Whatever choice you make makes you. Choose wisely."
- Roy T. Bennett

● **I'm thankful for** ....
....
....
....

● **Today I look forward to** ....
....
....
....

● **How can I make myself feel good today?** ....
....
....
....

● **What can I do today in order to bring me closer to my goals?** ....
....
....

● **What is the most important thing for me to do today?** ....
....
....

● **I am** ....
....
....
....

*"Lack of direction, not lack of time, is the problem.
We all have twenty-four hour days." - Zig Ziglar*

● *I'm thankful for* ....
....
....
....

● *Today I look forward to* ....
....
....
....

● *How can I make myself feel good today?* ....
....
....
....

● *What can I do today in order to bring me closer
to my goals?* ....
....
....

● *What is the most important thing for me to do
today?* ....
....
....

● *I am* ....
....
....
....

"The only way of discovering the limits of the possible is to venture a little way past them into the impossible." - Arthur C. Clarke

● *I'm thankful for* ....
....
....
....

● *Today I look forward to* ....
....
....
....

● *How can I make myself feel good today?* ....
....
....
....

● *What can I do today in order to bring me closer to my goals?* ....
....
....

● *What is the most important thing for me to do today?* ....
....
....

● *I am* ....
....
....
....

"Do not let the memories of your past limit the potential of your future. There are no limits to what you can achieve on your journey through life, except in your mind." - Roy T. Bennett

● *I'm thankful for* ....
....
....
....

● *Today I look forward to* ....
....
....
....

● *How can I make myself feel good today?* ....
....
....
....

● *What can I do today in order to bring me closer to my goals?* ....
....
....

● *What is the most important thing for me to do today?* ....
....
....

● *I am* ....
....
....
....

Do your thing!

Free Form / Brainstorm / Draw / Sketch
Doodle / Stream of Consciousness
Safe Space / Create / Vent / Manifest

Date: /   /

*"Be brave enough to live the life of your dreams
according to your vision and purpose instead of the
expectations and opinions of others."*
- Roy T. Bennett

● *I'm thankful for* ....
....
....
....

● *Today I look forward to* ....
....
....
....

● *How can I make myself feel good today?* ....
....
....
....

● *What can I do today in order to bring me closer
to my goals?* ....
....
....

● *What is the most important thing for me to do
today?* ....
....
....

● *I am* ....
....
....
....

"It's only after you've stepped outside your comfort zone that you begin to change, grow, and transform." - Roy T. Bennett

● *I'm thankful for* ....

....

....

....

● *Today I look forward to* ....

....

....

....

● *How can I make myself feel good today?* ....

....

....

....

● *What can I do today in order to bring me closer to my goals?* ....

....

....

● *What is the most important thing for me to do today?* ....

....

....

● *I am* ....

....

....

....

"Don't be pushed around by the fears in your mind.
Be led by the dreams in your heart."
- Roy T. Bennett

● *I'm thankful for* ....
....
....
....

● *Today I look forward to* ....
....
....
....

● *How can I make myself feel good today?* ....
....
....
....

● *What can I do today in order to bring me closer*
to my goals? ....
....
....

● *What is the most important thing for me to do*
today? ....
....
....

● *I am* ....
....
....
....

Date: / /

"Life is about accepting the challenges along the way, choosing to keep moving forward, and savoring the journey." - Roy T. Bennett

● *I'm thankful for* ....
....
....
....

● *Today I look forward to* ....
....
....
....

● *How can I make myself feel good today?* ....
....
....
....

● *What can I do today in order to bring me closer to my goals?* ....
....
....

● *What is the most important thing for me to do today?* ....
....
....

● *I am* ....
....
....
....

Date: / /

"Without ambition one starts nothing. Without work one finishes nothing. The prize will not be sent to you. You have to win it." - Ralph Waldo Emerson

● *I'm thankful for* ....
....
....
....

● *Today I look forward to* ....
....
....
....

● *How can I make myself feel good today?* ....
....
....
....

● *What can I do today in order to bring me closer to my goals?* ....
....
....

● *What is the most important thing for me to do today?* ....
....
....

● *I am* ....
....
....
....

Date: / /

⬢ *I'm thankful for* ....
....
....
....

⬢ *Today I look forward to* ....
....
....
....

⬢ *How can I make myself feel good today?* ....
....
....
....

⬢ *What can I do today in order to bring me closer to my goals?* ....
....
....

⬢ *What is the most important thing for me to do today?* ....
....
....

⬢ *I am* ....
....
....
....

"When the going gets tough, put one foot in front of the other and just keep going. Don't give up."
- Roy T. Bennett

● *I'm thankful for* ....
....
....
....

● *Today I look forward to* ....
....
....
....

● *How can I make myself feel good today?* ....
....
....
....

● *What can I do today in order to bring me closer to my goals?* ....
....
....

● *What is the most important thing for me to do today?* ....
....
....

● *I am* ....
....
....
....

Do your thing!

Free Form / Brainstorm / Draw / Sketch
Doodle / Stream of Consciousness
Safe Space / Create / Vent / Manifest

Date: / /

● *I'm thankful for* ....
....
....
....

● *Today I look forward to* ....
....
....
....

● *How can I make myself feel good today?* ....
....
....
....

● *What can I do today in order to bring me closer to my goals?* ....
....
....

● *What is the most important thing for me to do today?* ....
....
....

● *I am* ....
....
....
....

Date: / /

● *I'm thankful for* ....
....
....
....

● *Today I look forward to* ....
....
....
....

● *How can I make myself feel good today?* ....
....
....
....

● *What can I do today in order to bring me closer
to my goals?* ....
....
....

● *What is the most important thing for me to do
today?* ....
....
....

● *I am* ....
....
....
....

"Whatever the mind can conceive and believe, it can achieve." - Napoleon Hill

⬤ *I'm thankful for* ....
....
....
....

⬤ *Today I look forward to* ....
....
....
....

⬤ *How can I make myself feel good today?* ....
....
....
....

⬤ *What can I do today in order to bring me closer to my goals?* ....
....
....

⬤ *What is the most important thing for me to do today?* ....
....
....

⬤ *I am* ....
....
....
....

Date: / /

● *I'm thankful for* ....
....
....
....

● *Today I look forward to* ....
....
....
....

● *How can I make myself feel good today?* ....
....
....
....

● *What can I do today in order to bring me closer to my goals?* ....
....
....

● *What is the most important thing for me to do today?* ....
....
....

● *I am* ....
....
....
....

"It doesn't matter how many times you get knocked down. All that matters is you get up one more time than you were knocked down." - Roy T. Bennett

● *I'm thankful for* ....
....
....
....

● *Today I look forward to* ....
....
....
....

● *How can I make myself feel good today?* ....
....
....
....

● *What can I do today in order to bring me closer to my goals?* ....
....
....

● *What is the most important thing for me to do today?* ....
....
....

● *I am* ....
....
....
....

Date: /   /

"Don't wait for things to happen. Make them happen." - Roy T. Bennett

● *I'm thankful for* ....
....
....
....

● *Today I look forward to* ....
....
....
....

● *How can I make myself feel good today?* ....
....
....
....

● *What can I do today in order to bring me closer to my goals?* ....
....
....

● *What is the most important thing for me to do today?* ....
....
....

● *I am* ....
....
....
....

Date: / /

● *I'm thankful for* ....
....
....
....

● *Today I look forward to* ....
....
....
....

● *How can I make myself feel good today?* ....
....
....
....

● *What can I do today in order to bring me closer
to my goals?* ....
....
....

● *What is the most important thing for me to do
today?* ....
....
....

● *I am* ....
....
....
....

Do your thing!

Free Form / Brainstorm / Draw / Sketch
Doodle / Stream of Consciousness
Safe Space / Create / Vent / Manifest

"You are essentially who you create yourself to be and all that occurs in your life is the result of your own making." - Stephen Richards

● *I'm thankful for* ....
....
....
....

● *Today I look forward to* ....
....
....
....

● *How can I make myself feel good today?* ....
....
....
....

● *What can I do today in order to bring me closer to my goals?* ....
....
....

● *What is the most important thing for me to do today?* ....
....
....

● *I am* ....
....
....
....

*"First say to yourself what you would be and then
do what you have to do." - Epictetus*

● *I'm thankful for* ....
....
....
....

● *Today I look forward to* ....
....
....
....

● *How can I make myself feel good today?* ....
....
....
....

● *What can I do today in order to bring me closer
to my goals?* ....
....
....

● *What is the most important thing for me to do
today?* ....
....
....

● *I am* ....
....
....
....

Date: / /

● *I'm thankful for* ....
....
....
....

● *Today I look forward to* ....
....
....
....

● *How can I make myself feel good today?* ....
....
....
....

● *What can I do today in order to bring me closer to my goals?* ....
....
....

● *What is the most important thing for me to do today?* ....
....
....

● *I am* ....
....
....
....

Date: / /

● *I'm thankful for* ....
....
....
....

● *Today I look forward to* ....
....
....
....

● *How can I make myself feel good today?* ....
....
....
....

● *What can I do today in order to bring me closer to my goals?* ....
....
....

● *What is the most important thing for me to do today?* ....
....
....

● *I am* ....
....
....
....

Date: / /

"Act the way you'd like to be and soon you'll be the way you'd like to act." - Bob Dylan

● *I'm thankful for* ....
....
....
....

● *Today I look forward to* ....
....
....
....

● *How can I make myself feel good today?* ....
....
....
....

● *What can I do today in order to bring me closer to my goals?* ....
....
....

● *What is the most important thing for me to do today?* ....
....
....

● *I am* ....
....
....
....

Date: / /

● *I'm thankful for* ....
....
....
....

● *Today I look forward to* ....
....
....
....

● *How can I make myself feel good today?* ....
....
....
....

● *What can I do today in order to bring me closer to my goals?* ....
....
....

● *What is the most important thing for me to do today?* ....
....
....

● *I am* ....
....
....
....

Date: / /

⬡ *I'm thankful for* ....
....
....
....

⬡ *Today I look forward to* ....
....
....
....

⬡ *How can I make myself feel good today?* ....
....
....
....

⬡ *What can I do today in order to bring me closer to my goals?* ....
....
....

⬡ *What is the most important thing for me to do today?* ....
....
....

⬡ *I am* ....
....
....
....

Do your thing!

Free Form / Brainstorm / Draw / Sketch
Doodle / Stream of Consciousness
Safe Space / Create / Vent / Manifest

Date: / /

"If you can't believe in miracles, then believe in yourself." - Isabel Lopez

● *I'm thankful for* ....
....
....
....

● *Today I look forward to* ....
....
....
....

● *How can I make myself feel good today?*.............
....
....
....

● *What can I do today in order to bring me closer to my goals?*...
....
....

● *What is the most important thing for me to do today?*...
....
....

● *I am* ....
....
....
....

"Most people fail in life not because they aim too high and miss, but because they aim too low and hit." - Les Brown

⬢ *I'm thankful for* ....
....
....
....

⬢ *Today I look forward to* ....
....
....
....

⬢ *How can I make myself feel good today?* ....
....
....
....

⬢ *What can I do today in order to bring me closer to my goals?* ....
....
....

⬢ *What is the most important thing for me to do today?* ....
....
....

⬢ *I am* ....
....
....
....

> *"Your beliefs affect your choices. Your choices shape your actions. Your actions determine your results."* - Roy T. Bennett

● *I'm thankful for* ....
....
....
....

● *Today I look forward to* ....
....
....
....

● *How can I make myself feel good today?* ....
....
....
....

● *What can I do today in order to bring me closer to my goals?* ....
....
....

● *What is the most important thing for me to do today?* ....
....
....

● *I am* ....
....
....
....

"The greatest revenge is massive success."
- Les Brown

⬣ *I'm thankful for* ....
....
....
....

⬣ *Today I look forward to* ....
....
....
....

⬣ *How can I make myself feel good today?* ....
....
....
....

⬣ *What can I do today in order to bring me closer*
to my goals? ....
....
....

⬣ *What is the most important thing for me to do*
today? ....
....
....

⬣ *I am* ....
....
....
....

"The most powerful magic of all is choice."
- Sara Raasch, Ice Like Fire

● *I'm thankful for* ....
....
....
....

● *Today I look forward to* ....
....
....
....

● *How can I make myself feel good today?* ....
....
....
....

● *What can I do today in order to bring me closer*
to my goals? ....
....
....

● *What is the most important thing for me to do*
today? ....
....
....

● *I am* ....
....
....
....

Date: / /

"Make the choice to embrace this day. Do not let your TODAY be stolen by the ghost of yesterday or the "To-Do" list of tomorrow!" - Steve Maraboli

● *I'm thankful for* ....
....
....
....

● *Today I look forward to* ....
....
....
....

● *How can I make myself feel good today?* ....
....
....
....

● *What can I do today in order to bring me closer to my goals?* ....
....
....

● *What is the most important thing for me to do today?* ....
....
....

● *I am* ....
....
....
....

Date: / /

"Shoot for the moon, because even if you miss, you'll land in the stars." - Les Brown

● *I'm thankful for* ....
....
....
....

● *Today I look forward to* ....
....
....
....

● *How can I make myself feel good today?* ....
....
....
....

● *What can I do today in order to bring me closer to my goals?* ....
....
....

● *What is the most important thing for me to do today?* ....
....
....

● *I am* ....
....
....
....

Do your thing!

Free Form / Brainstorm / Draw / Sketch
Doodle / Stream of Consciousness
Safe Space / Create / Vent / Manifest

Do your thing!

Free Form / Brainstorm / Draw / Sketch
Doodle / Stream of Consciousness
Safe Space / Create / Vent / Manifest

Complete your Legend

Available from Legendary Life

Journals

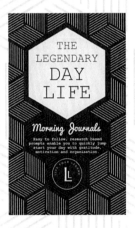

Affirmation Cards